In *Amina's Third Eye*, Amina utilizes meditation to contact her ancestors. These ancestral connections will assist her in transforming her community which is filled with grief and sorrow, into a manifestation of joy, wealth, health, and togetherness.

Written by
**Dynast Amir**
Illustrated by
**Yashar Clemons**

# Amina's Third Eye:

## FOREWORD

***"Children's children are a crown to the aged, and parents are the pride of their children." Proverbs 17:6 (NIV)***

As a serial entrepreneur, who has worked for a Fortune 500 company and has a background in marketing, branding, and public relations, it was a humbling call to receive from Dynast Amir to assist with the launch of *Amina's Third Eye: A Children's Story on Manifestation through Meditation.* We've been friends for almost a decade and share a mutual connection of love, respect, regard and esteem for each other. When Dynast described *Amina's Third Eye*, my immediate response was elation. I too was uncovering the *Power of Meditation & Manifestation.* Often feeling childlike myself, I connected with the characteristics of Amina's life, culture, and journey.

Growing up in an impoverished environment, I understood all too well the wanting to provide a better way of life for my family and community. Just as Amina, we all search for the "answer" to the universal question, "Who am I?" Often times the answer we seek lies within. Through meditation, we allow the Universe to open the door to endless possibilities.

After reading *Amina's Third Eye*, you will learn how meditation provides an escape from stress, anxiety, and nervousness to return you to the same carefree attitude once known in childhood. *Amina's Third Eye* allows readers to gain the basic principles of elevation and creation in simple language. Regardless of age, reading level, or experience, anyone can grasp these concepts and benefit from the progress. Enjoy!

**~ Jenee Mogul**

*The Voices of the ancestors are the voices of the Gods.*

**~ African Proverb**

One day in African history class, Amina was given teachings on the past.

African people had gold & diamonds
piled to the sky.
But in her neighborhood, families
barely get by.

She learned that Africa is the
richest land on earth,
But in her neighborhood, kids
didn't value their own self-worth.

She learned that the Greeks, Romans, and Persians came to Africa to learn by the masses.

But in her neighborhood, many refused to go to classes.

When class was over, Amina caught the bus home.

When Amina arrived home, she asked her parents and her brother Mansa, "Can we ask the Africans of the past, to show us how to make our communities rich again and this time make them last?"

"Yes Amina. You can," replied her mom. "The ancestors are alive inside of you. You can contact them through meditation and they will guide you."

Amina's father added, "Once you connect to the ancestors, your *Third Eye* will open. This eye will help you build the community that you are hoping."

"*Third Eye*, I only have two. Where is this *Third Eye*," Amina questioned? Her father replied, "It is hidden in the center of your mind, opening this eye would make you all wise."

Mansa then commented, "The secrets to manifesting the community we need lies inside of you. Once they are revealed, this community could be like ancient Africa too."

Amina grew anxious to get started. She left the dinner table went outside and sat under the *Touba* tree in her yard.

She stated her purpose to the ancestors. She described, "How she wanted to transform her community into an *Utopia* called H.O.P.E.," which stands for *Heaven On Planet Earth*.

She then went into silence. Her head was now clear. She felt that the spirits of the ancestors were near. The ancestors soon appeared to Amina in a vision. They said, "We are here to help you on your mission."

The ancestor Makeda, "Queen of Sheba," told Amina, "In order to build H.O.P.E., you need to motivate the people. The community should never settle for average; they should always strive to be great."

Then the ancestor Tiye, "Queen of Egypt," told Amina, "In order to rule you must first serve, this is how you earn the respect that you deserve."

The ancestor Nandi, "Queen of Zululand," added, "Be generous, honest, fair, and cool. If the people see you as cool, you will always rule."

Finally, the ancestor, Nzinga "Queen of Ndongo and Matamba," said, "Amina, never quit. Whatever you set your mind to, you can manifest it."

When Amina awoke from her meditation, all the ancestors affirmed, "We are here to help you manifest *Heaven On Planet Earth*."

Amina opened her eyes and proclaimed, "The time is now to begin, to build an utopia for our loved ones and a safe haven for our beloved children again!!!"

Amina went out into her community, gathered the people and declared, "This community is going to become the *Promised Land*, where the word can't will be replaced with the word can!!!"

Inspired by Amina, the community immediately built beautiful homes and planted farms.

Now everyone had shelter and ate healthy food instead of fast food that does the body harm.

Secondly, the residents opened businesses and provided jobs for all in need.

Now everyone had plenty of money indeed.

Thirdly, the community built schools to teach kids how to build a powerful nation.
And if ever challenged, taught them how to defend their nation.

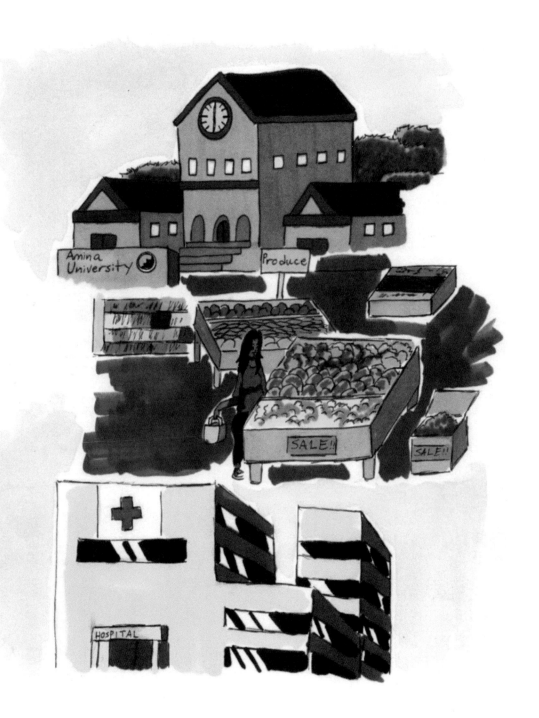

Finally, the people built hospitals, grocery stores, and universities. The ancestors blessed Amina's city, for they could not have been more pleased.

At last, *Heaven On Planet Earth* was realized.
It manifested, for Amina connected to her ancestors through the opening of her *Third Eye*.

# THE END

# Amina's Third Eye:

## Author's Note

I want kids to internalize the concept of living life from the inside out. In the $3^{rd}$ grade before my track meets, I would close my eyes and imagine myself winning my events before I competed in them. Once I completed these imaginative rituals, I would enter my sprints confident that I would win $1^{st}$ place. The abundance of gold medals in my house proves that I was often triumphant. In the $3^{rd}$ grade I didn't refer to this ritual as meditation, but I knew that there was a power behind utilizing my imagination as an effective channel for manifestation. Through meditation, kids can take their innermost desires and manifest them into their outermost reality. If children were to close their eyes, focus on their goals, ask the ancestors for help to accomplish their goals, and then actively pursue their specific goals relentlessly, they would fulfill everything that their hearts' desire. In fulfilling their objectives, the children will usher in H.O.P.E., *Heaven On Planet Earth*, for the children are the only future that the human race has.

## ~Dynast Amir

Special thanks to my Mom, Dad, Ancestors, Bro. Ibrahim Jallow, Ekemma, Jenee for the foreword, Yashar for the illustrations and Natalia for adding the finishing touches.

# Amina's Third Eye:

**Dynast Amir** was born in Sacramento, CA. He found his passion for writing through journaling everyday. Dynast has been consistently traveling to Africa since 2011, and plans on relocating to Nigeria and Sierra Leone soon. His ambition in life is to purchase lands for afflicted souls and to possess more gold than Mansa Musa. Dynast currently serves as the Omo Oba "Prince" of Ororuwo, Nigeria and invites everyone to come and visit the Kingdom of Ororuwo one day.

**Yashar Clemons** is a native of Los Angeles, CA. Just recently graduating from Chico State University in Chico, California, he is in the process of debuting his own comic book series. Yashar's ambition is to be a professional animator and to uplift souls through art. In accomplishing this, he believes that he will experience true happiness. "I want to make a living doing what I love to do best."

# Amina's Third Eye:

Manufactured in the United States of America

ISBN: 978-1-7346383-5-6

Publisher/Author contact: info@noirisme.com

For information regarding discounts or bulk purchases, please visit our website or email info@noirisme.com

# Amina's Third Eye:

Made in the USA
Las Vegas, NV
02 March 2024

86576612R00033